THE UNIVERSITY COLL...

DRAGONS
◁ MYTHS AND LEGENDS ▷

Translated by Abigail Frost

Illustrations by Francis Phillipps

Written and edited by Gilles Ragache

CHERRYTREE BOOKS

A Cherrytree Book

Adapted by A S Publishing
from *Les Dragons*
published by Hachette
© 1989, Hachette, Paris

First published 1990
by Cherrytree Press Ltd
a subsidiary of
The Chivers Company Ltd
Windsor Bridge Road
Bath, Avon BA2 3AX

Reprinted 1992

Copyright © Cherrytree Press Ltd 1990

British Library Cataloguing in Publication Data
Dragons.
   1. Legends. Special subjects : Dragons
   I. Frost, Abigail   II. Series
   398.469

   ISBN 0-7451-5108-6

Printed in Hong Kong by Colorcraft Ltd

▷ CONTENTS ◁

▷ THE BROKEN SWORD ◁

Regin the dwarf beat his hammer rhythmically against the anvil, slowly forging a perfect blade. His wrinkled face, tanned by years at the forge, shone with pearls of sweat. He worked slowly and carefully, watched all the time by young Siegfried, to whom he was teaching the secrets of his craft. Many years ago, the boy's mother, Sieglinde, had been lost in the forest. She was just about to give birth to her son. The dwarf had rescued her, and later become the boy's tutor, teaching him to be a great warrior. He taught Siegfried the arts of battle and of hunting: how to track stags and kill wolves and bears. He gave him a spirited grey stallion to ride, and Siegfried became a fine horseman, galloping through the vast forests.

This morning, after his ride, Siegfried took less notice than usual of his lessons. He seemed preoccupied. When Regin asked what the matter was, the boy said he had heard strange sounds in the forest. Regin at once forbade Siegfried to return to the place where he had heard the noises. It was unlucky. But next day, the boy rode there again. The noises were louder this time, but he could not see who or what was making them.

Siegfried owned up to his disobedience and asked Regin to explain. Realising that he could

The broken sword had belonged to Siegfried's father, and before him to Wotan, most powerful of the gods. It had magic powers . . .

He had given him a spirited grey stallion to ride, and Siegfried became a fine horseman galloping through vast forests.

not hide the truth from his pupil, the dwarf told him that a great dragon, Fafnir, lived there, guarding a hoard of fabulous treasure. The hoard contained a gold ring and a magic helmet that brought wealth and immortal life to whoever owned them. But nobody who had tried to fight the dragon had ever come back.

Seeing that his warning could not deter young Siegfried, Regin decided to reveal another secret. For months, at his forge, he had been working on one weapon: a sword, broken into three, which only long hours of painstaking work might repair. This, he explained, was Siegfried's father's sword. It had been broken in his last, terrible battle, a few months before Siegfried was born. That was why Siegfried had never seen his father.

Before Siegfried's father had owned it, the sword had belonged to Wotan, most powerful of the gods. The sword had magic powers, and

its name was Nothung. Siegfried took the hammer from the dwarf, and set about finishing the work. After several days, the pieces were joined invisibly. The blade was stronger than it had been before.

Siegfried set out for the dragon's lair. He could still see no sign of the beast, but he could hear its voice – snarls that would freeze the blood of the most hardened knight. As he pressed forward, Siegfried's horse sensed danger: it stopped and refused to go further.

Prudently, Siegfried took heed of his horse, and turned back to fetch Regin and Nothung. The dwarf had long expected the moment when his foster-son would go to fight the dragon. He had been preparing Siegfried for this battle since he was born. The old dwarf was suddenly afraid: was the sword really strong enough? Would Siegfried be the victor in this fight to the death?

5

Lightning flashed from Siegfried's magic sword, and knocked the dragon down.

SIEGFRIED

GUARDIAN OF THE MAGIC RING

Fafnir, deep in his lair, watched the road in silence. He had sensed an intruder. At last a young knight, riding a fiery grey stallion, appeared on the way to his cave. Though very young, he seemed confident; he carried a shining, strangely-wrought sword. At his side marched an ancient, red-faced dwarf – an old acquaintance. 'Regin!' breathed the dragon. 'I've got him at last!'

Pretending not to notice, the dragon let the new challengers approach. The young knight dismounted and sprang to the attack. But his blows were ineffectual. The sword simply slipped off Fafnir's armoured skin.

Then Fafnir felt a stab of pain as the youth stabbed his shoulder. Enraged, he drew a deep breath, then let out a torrent of fire. The dwarf, and the horse, caught in the flames, died at once – but Siegfried got away.

Though badly burned on his face and arms,

Siegfried ignored the pain: he had seen his two best friends die horribly. He was fired with anger. Death held no terror for him – all he wanted now was vengeance.

Slowly Fafnir drew near, determined to go for the kill. He drew a deep breath. Flames played around his mouth. Siegfried stood firm, praying to the gods to help him in his struggle. He raised his magic sword Nothung. Lightning flashed from the blade; the bolt sped across the cave, and knocked the dragon down. Blinded and shocked, Fafnir rolled on his back and beat his claws against the empty air. Siegfried moved in for the final blow. The dragon never rose again.

Siegfried thanked the gods for their help and, still amazed to be alive, kissed the blade of Nothung, drenched in the dragon's blood. At once he felt his own blood stir and started: he could understand the language of the birds.

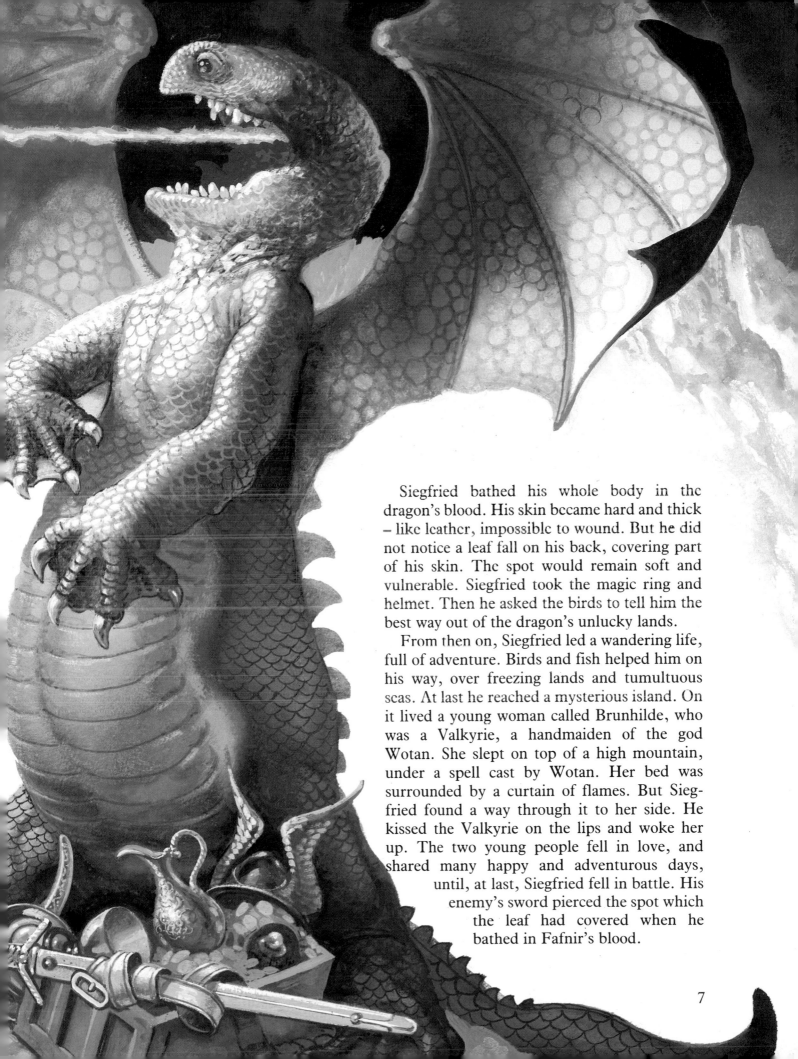

Siegfried bathed his whole body in the dragon's blood. His skin became hard and thick – like leather, impossible to wound. But he did not notice a leaf fall on his back, covering part of his skin. The spot would remain soft and vulnerable. Siegfried took the magic ring and helmet. Then he asked the birds to tell him the best way out of the dragon's unlucky lands.

From then on, Siegfried led a wandering life, full of adventure. Birds and fish helped him on his way, over freezing lands and tumultuous seas. At last he reached a mysterious island. On it lived a young woman called Brunhilde, who was a Valkyrie, a handmaiden of the god Wotan. She slept on top of a high mountain, under a spell cast by Wotan. Her bed was surrounded by a curtain of flames. But Siegfried found a way through it to her side. He kissed the Valkyrie on the lips and woke her up. The two young people fell in love, and shared many happy and adventurous days, until, at last, Siegfried fell in battle. His enemy's sword pierced the spot which the leaf had covered when he bathed in Fafnir's blood.

TRISTAN AND ISEULT

THE SWALLOWS' MESSAGE

Long ago, when King Arthur ruled at Camelot, his cousin Mark, King of Cornwall was being pressed by his lords to marry. But none of the ladies he met seemed right. Some were beautiful but graceless; others were amusing but foolish; others were wise, but not loving. Mark wished he had not promised to make up his mind by that evening. In his heart, he did not want to marry anyone.

As Mark gazed out at the setting sun, two swallows flew in through the castle window. They circled round and dropped something down to him. Then they twittered goodbye and flew away. Mark picked up their gift – a lock of perfect golden hair. As the lords lined up to hear his choice, Mark gave a sly smile. 'I have had a sign from heaven! I shall marry the lady whose hair this is!'

The lords passed the hair from hand to hand; none of them knew whose it was. But Tristan, Mark's nephew, knew at once: 'Only one lady in the world has such beautiful hair: Iseult, daughter of King Gormond!'

The lords gasped aloud; Gormond, the King of Ireland, was their king's enemy. He would never give Mark his daughter's hand. Some suspected that Tristan wanted to stop Mark marrying, and inherit the kingdom himself. But Tristan spoke up bravely: 'Tomorrow I shall sail for Ireland and fetch her!'

The lords knew that Tristan was risking his life. Last year, Tristan had killed Iseult's uncle, the evil Morholt, and Gormond wanted his life in exchange. His sword had lost a chip of steel in the fight. Some called him a fool, but he stood his ground. Sadly King Mark gave Tristan permission to sail.

Tristan landed at Wexford, to find the people gathering their possessions and fleeing as fast as they could. A terrified merchant told him they were running from a man-eating dragon. King Gormond had promised his daughter's hand in marriage to the man who killed it, but all who tried had died.

Tristan saw his chance and rode towards the dragon's lair, deep in a lonely marsh. Suddenly another knight galloped past in the opposite direction, too frightened to stop and speak. A sulphurous stench filled the air – and the dragon came into view!

Tristan spurred on his terrified horse. He had surprise on his side. The dragon, having just seen off one challenger, did not expect another so soon. Tristan thrust his lance into

Tristan saw his chance and rode towards the dragon's lair. Suddenly another knight galloped past.

the monster's throat and drew blood. The dragon stiffened, breaking the lance, and blew out a torrent of fire.

Tristan's horse died under him, as he retreated from the flames. He was half-suffocated, and his hands were burnt. Acrid, blinding smoke stung his eyes; he could not see to beat off the dragon's vicious claws. He fell down thinking this was the end.

The dragon, sure of winning, rolled its victim over and opened its mouth to eat him up. But Tristan, with one last burst of energy, sat up and stabbed his sword into the soft flesh of the monster's mouth. The dragon howled, and crawled away to die.

Tristan forgot his pain; victory roused him like wine. Rejoicing, he cut out the dragon's tongue, as proof that he had killed it. Next he looked for a stream, to quench his thirst and soothe his burnt skin. But he had not gone far when he collapsed in agony, poisoned by the dragon's venom.

WHO KILLED THE DRAGON?

Hiding under a tree some distance away was the knight who had passed Tristan on his way. Now that the dragon was silent, and it was safe to go out, he went to see what had happened. He found the dragon's body, but no sign of its killer. The dragon must have eaten him, he thought, and then died itself from its wounds. What a chance! The knight cut off the dragon's head and rode quickly to the king's palace.

Surprised that this cowardly knight should have killed the dragon, when so many brave men had failed, the king decided to wait before he gave Iseult away. Iseult, aghast at the thought of marrying this man, slipped out with her mother and maid, to find out what had happened for herself.

The women crossed the evil dragon's lands, until at last they came to its stinking, headless body. There they found Tristan's shield, and searched until they found him. Though unconscious, he was still just alive. They took him to the palace, and bathed him in the healing juices of magic herbs. Slowly his wounds healed, and his burnt skin grew whole again.

Iseult found herself attracted to this strange, handsome knight, and sat for hours by his side. To pass the time, she cleaned the dragon's thick blood from his sword, and recognised the chip in its blade. It fitted a fragment of metal which had lodged in her uncle Morholt's skull. Tristan must have killed him! To avenge her family, Iseult moved towards the sleeping knight, to stab him with his own sword.

But as the blade touched him, Tristan woke – and Iseult hesitated. She recognised him now, even though he had been disguised as a minstrel on his earlier visit. But he was very ill and she pitied him. She asked why he had come back. Moved by his story, she persuaded her father to forgive him Morholt's death, and hear his case against the other knight who claimed to have killed the dragon.

The king asked each knight to show his evidence. The cowardly knight showed the dragon's head, but Tristan had its tongue! Convinced by Tristan's story, the king banished the other knight from his kingdom.

Tristan had achieved his quest. The king agreed to let Iseult marry Mark, and to make peace between Ireland and Cornwall. But Iseult's heart was disappointed; she had begun to love Tristan. Her mother realised this, and to make her daughter love her husband, mixed a magic potion, which she gave to Iseult's maid. But the maid – who knows why? – put it into a

The cowardly knight showed the dragon's head, but Tristan had its tongue!

drink which Tristan and Iseult shared during the voyage home. Its power made them love each other so much that they would die if parted.

Tristan's triumph had ended in tragedy. Iseult married Mark – who had never wanted to be married at all – but loved Tristan, who could never leave her side until death.

11

SAINT GEORGE AND THE DRAGON

Once upon a time, the people of Sylene, a town in Libya, lived in fear of a huge dragon. It hid in the desert near the town walls and sneaked up to the gates to catch passers-by unawares. It poisoned them with its breath before eating them up. Soon nobody dared enter or leave the town, the town's trade vanished and famine threatened. So the townsfolk decided to appease the monster with tribute. First, they offered a dozen white ewes. Satisfied and full, the dragon disappeared for three months . . . but then it came back.

They offered more sheep and the dragon took them, and then more. Each time it became greedier, taking first dozens, then hundreds. The shepherds were ruined.

When all the sheep had been eaten, the dragon ordered the townsfolk to send it their young people. Its appetite for fresh meat grew by the day, until nothing could satisfy the beast. The people sent the fairest young girls of the town to be eaten, sadly making this sacrifice to stop the dragon attacking. At last the dragon demanded the fairest maiden of all: the king's daughter, the princess Sabra.

One grey morning, the princess went to meet her fate. Growling with delight, the dragon led her off to its desert lair.

It happened that day that a young knight called George was riding by. When he heard the sad news, George galloped off to the cave where the dragon took its innocent prey. At first he followed the dragon's tracks, but as he drew nearer, he could hear the princess's cries and

Sabra led the dragon like a gigantic pet lizard on a lead.

the dragon's growls. He reached them just as the dragon opened its mouth to swallow Sabra.

The knight brandished his lance; on its point fluttered a banner, white with a red cross. 'A coat of arms – he must be serving a great lord,' thought Princess Sabra, who had never seen a knight bearing a cross before.

With a loud war-cry, George attacked. The dragon drew back in surprise – who dared challenge it in its own land? Who dared disturb it when such a feast was in sight?

The dragon turned instantly to face its brave and unexpected enemy. It stared at George, hoping to hold him petrified, but George twisted and turned to avoid its hypnotic eye.

George charged and struck the dragon. He wounded it but his lance stuck in the thick skin and broke. Dismounting, he fought bravely on foot, sword in hand. Again he wounded the dragon, but it hardly seemed to notice, and fought on with its vicious claws. The battle seemed lost; but then George called on his lord for help. For the first time, Sabra heard the name of Jesus.

What happened next was a miracle: the dragon walked back a few steps, bowed its head and lay on the ground in submission!

Sabra did not believe her eyes. She was rooted to the spot by fear. George ordered her to take off her silken sash and tie it round the monster's neck. Trembling, she obeyed. To her great surprise, the dragon, now tame, did not resist. George and Sabra brought the dragon back to the town like a gigantic pet on a lead.

The people of Sylene rejoiced and the king declared a feast in George's honour. When the king asked what reward he would like, George said that the city's safety was enough, but he hoped that the people would now become Christians. Next day they were all baptised, and George and the princess were married. He became the protector of the now-prosperous town. But one fine day, he left as he had arrived, alone on his horse, off to far countries in search of adventures.

13

▷ DRAGONS

Many naturalists have wanted to observe the dragon in its natural habitat, but few have succeeded. Still, if you want to try, the old legends give plenty of useful information and advice.

Where dragons hide
Dragons, being mysterious, fierce animals, are always difficult to see. They are choosy about where they live. Unless you are like St George, you would not be likely to meet one in a desert – much too hot and dry for them! Dragons like the damp, and always live where there is plenty of water. They like to guard springs and old, forgotten wells (1). In the Far East, they like to live in rushing rivers, at the bottom of the sea, or deep inside thunder-clouds. When the thunder sounds and the lightning flashes, they are truly in their element (2). In the Middle Ages, they preferred to live far from towns and the bustle of humanity deep in dark, damp caves (3), or in thick forests where they could watch out for their prey (4). If you should be travelling through such dangerous places, watch out! There may be a dragon about!

Watchful eyes
Western dragons (these are the dangerous ones) eat and drink a lot, but they never sleep (5). They watch over their

OBSERVED ◁

treasures day and night. Some of them do not even have eyelids. The Greeks linked them with Athena, the goddess of wisdom, because wisdom is always watchful.

Eastern dragons are not so unpleasant, but they are very greedy, and love to get drunk; and they certainly go to sleep, in fact some are downright lazy and sleep for months on end.

If you find yourself under the nose of a dragon, first make sure which kind it is. But whatever the answer, you are in grave danger. A look from a dragons's eye can paralyse you (6), unless you have you are carrying the proper charms or can recite the correct spells. Better not to go near enough to see the whites of its eyes.

Foul mouths

Even at a respectable distance, even fast asleep, dragons are still dangerous (7). Most of them can spit fire (8) which destroys everything around. Wear a good helmet and carry a fire-proof shield if you want to observe a fire-breather.

Even worse, a dragon's breath is poisonous; an invisible danger to the foolhardy naturalist. The terrible fumes it breathes out can kill instantly. So, if you find a dragon, be extremely careful; take the best weapons, never look one of the beasts in the eye, and hold your breath!

Before he even met the dragon, Jason had to fight a giant.

GUARDIAN OF THE GOLDEN FLEECE

The good ship *Argo* sped over the waves with a following wind, a trail of white foam in her wake. She was the greatest ship of the Greek world. Jason, her captain, stood on the prow, scanning the horizon for the mysterious shore of Colchis. Throughout the long hard voyage, Jason had never gone far from the prow. The prow was enchanted, cut from a sacred oak. When danger threatened, it would speak to him, to guide him through reefs or even foretell the future.

Cheated of his kingdom by his half-brother Pelias, Jason had been sailing unknown seas for years, seeking the famous Golden Fleece that was hidden in Colchis. The wicked Pelias had agreed to return Jason's lands if he brought back this treasure. It was the fleece of a ram sacred to Zeus, but all who tried to take it died a violent death. The King of Colchis had set a fearsome dragon to guard the fleece. Pelias thought that Jason, like all the others, would never be seen again. But Jason was determined to succeed in his quest. He had brought together the finest crew in Greece. Every one of his sailors, the Argonauts, was a famous hero. Amongst them were Theseus who had slain a monster, the twins Castor and Pollux, the musician Orpheus, and Herakles, the strongest man in the world. They and many more heroes had agreed to sail with Jason on his daring quest.

'Land ahead!' cried Jason. All the Argonauts rushed to see: the fleece would soon be within their grasp, or so they thought. But when they landed, the cruel king set Jason many tasks before allowing him even to set eyes on the fleece. First he had to fight fearsome fire-breathing bulls, then giants with enormous clubs. He was not alone in his trials. He was helped by the king's daughter Medea, who had fallen in love with him.

When Jason saw the Golden Fleece nailed to a sacred oak tree, he thought he had won. But he thought too soon. A fierce dragon surged from its cave spitting flames at him. Brave as he was, the fire was more than he could stand. All seemed lost, but Medea knew what to do. She rubbed Jason all over with a magic ointment and gave him a mysterious bunch of leaves to hold, and magic spells to use. Alone, Jason went forward to meet the dragon.

Again the dragon went for him. But, this time, Jason walked fearlessly into the flames, his shield on his arm. Blinded by the monster's burning breath, Jason repeated the magic

words. The heat was almost unbearable, and he thought himself lost. But suddenly the bunch of leaves caught fire and gave out a blue, scented smoke. Inhaling the smoke the dragon became sleepy, and fell with a great crash to the ground, where it lay harmlessly snoring. Without delay Jason took the Golden Fleece and ran to the *Argo* with Medea.

The waiting Argonauts cast off the ship, and rowed like slaves away from the coast. Back in Iolcus, after a long and perilous voyage, Jason regained his kingdom and married Medea; but the Golden Fleece brought only fleeting happiness. Medea proved cruel and jealous, ready to kill anyone who got in her way. In the end, Jason left her and set off on new adventures.

Blinded by the monster's burning breath, Jason spoke Medea's spells . . .

17

CLEOSTRATOS'S ARMOUR

Like all his friends, the young Greek Cleostratos had grown up in fear. A dragon had been ravaging the country for years. Once a year it demanded tribute, the life of a fine young man. Each year, when the terrible decision had to be made, the young men drew lots to choose who was to die.

Eventually, Cleostratos drew the fatal lot. His friends wept, but he accepted his fate bravely. Then his best friend, Menestratos, spoke: 'Don't just give in quietly to this horrible fate! I've an idea . . .'

The two young men took to spending long hours alone in the armourer's forge. Nobody could guess what they were doing, but they were using huge amounts of leather and iron.

On the appointed day, Cleostratos dressed in secret. First he put on what they had been making – a strange harness of leather, covered in sharp iron spikes. Then he put on a heavy tunic to hide the armour.

All the townspeople stood on the walls to watch Cleostratos walk to his doom, head held high. The dragon appeared. Seemingly unarmed, Cleostratos stood perfectly still and did not resist. He did not want to draw the dragon's fire.

Luckily, the dragon was a greedy one. It could hardly wait to devour its prey. It leaped upon Cleostratos and swallowed him whole. Then how it howled! The spectators saw it twist and writhe, and throw itself to the ground in agony. Cleostratos's armour was tearing its insides to pieces! Menestratos and the bravest young men set on the howling monster. They cut open its stomach and pulled out the body of their brave friend. Cleostratos was given a solemn burial, and the town was never again bothered by dragons.

Cleostratos put on his strange armour.

Triptolemus's tame dragons were faster and more spirited than any horse he had ever driven.

TRIPTOLEMUS'S CHARIOT

Demeter, the Earth goddess, came to Eleusis, where the king received her kindly. Staying at his palace, she made friends with young Triptolemus, and taught him all her secret wisdom. When it was time for her to leave, she called Triptolemus and said, 'You will take these seeds to the people of Greece, and teach them how to grow wheat. And here is something to help you reach even the remotest islands!' She showed him her present. It was the finest chariot he had ever seen, and harnessed to it were beautiful winged dragons!

Triptolemus and his dragons became famous throughout Greece. As his fame spread, princes became envious. Some offered fortunes for his chariot and dragons. Others threatened violence.

Lyncos, the King of Scythia, tried to kill the boy who had taught him the secrets of agriculture. He stole into his room by night with a sword in his hand. But watchful Demeter turned the murderous king into a wild cat – which we now call a lynx. Another king, Carnabon, invited Triptolemus to stay, then suddenly attacked him and killed one of the dragons. Demeter swept him up into the sky before he could do further harm. The son of King Eumelos of Patras stole the chariot – but he could not control the dragon and was hurled into the sun. Demeter was always watching over Triptolemus on his journey.

HUNTING

It isn't easy to kill a dragon, even for the bravest among us. Many dragon-hunters have resorted to tricks. Being so greedy, dragons can easily be fooled by a weapon hidden in something they like to eat.

Cow 'pow'

On the borders of France and Spain, a dragon with a huge mouth used to swallow cows whole to save carrying them off to its cave (1). The farmers desperately asked a clever knight for help. He watched the creature for many days, then asked the village women to sew some skins together to make a huge cow. Then he stuffed the cow with gunpowder, and took it to the dragon's cave, attached to a long fuse.

He lit the fuse and galloped away on his horse. Hearing the sound, the dragon looked out, saw the cow and swallowed it. Soon after, there was a mighty explosion, and the dragon never troubled the farmers again.

Bread of death

In the south of France (2), a man hid a sword in a long loaf of bread, which he left lying on a bridge where the dragon often went. The dragon picked up this tasty snack, swallowed it and died.

3

1

2

20

THE DRAGON

Deadly drinks from a goddess

The goddess Inara, worshipped by the Hittites of ancient Anatolia, took the shape of a beautiful princess and invited a terrifying dragon to a feast (3). The dragon, who liked nothing better than good food and pretty women, accepted at once. But when it got there, she gave it so much to drink that it fell down dead drunk, and never returned to its cave.

Brave bandit

A bandit in the Middle Ages offered to atone for his crimes by hiding in a huge barrel with holes in it (4). The people rolled the barrel down to the dragon's cave. The dragon swallowed the barrel without a moment's thought. Deep inside the dragon's stomach (it was very hot and almost airless), the bandit slid knives through the holes in the barrel. The dragon felt terrible pains in its stomach, and vomited up the barrel (complete with bandit); then it decided that the food in this place was terrible, and flew away.

Dragon raising

In ancient China (5), dragon festivals were noisy affairs. Everyone beat gongs and drums and let off firecrackers. They wanted to wake up the dragons that rule nature after their long winter sleep. People danced around in a great procession, carrying lanterns and papier-mâché dragons.

4

5

SUSANOWO

THE DRAGON WITH EIGHT HEADS

Silently the rider watched the farm, nestled in a deep valley behind a curtain of trees. The buildings were well looked-after and tidy, like all good Japanese houses, but no-one seemed to live there. Then the horseman heard muffled sobs. Curious, he drew his sword and rode into the farmyard, to find two old people and a beautiful young girl.

'Why these tears?' he asked.

The peasants hesitated, alarmed by the arrival of this fierce warrior. Then, after a ritual bow on either side, the old man spoke. Still sobbing, he presented his wife and daughter, Kunisada. She was the last of eight daughters.

All the others had been eaten, one by one, by a hideous eight-headed dragon. 'And at midnight tonight, the dragon is coming for Kunisada!'

They did not know that the handsome horseman was Susanowo, the god of storms. He had led a stormy life, too, and was not always generous and friendly. Now he had been thrown from heaven by his sister Amaterasu for upsetting everyone. But he could see how distressed these people were, and how beautiful Kunisada was. A brave and valiant fighter, he could not bear to go on his way leaving them to face the dragon. But even for him, it would be a dangerous task. As he hesitated, he heard a

distant roar, like thunder. 'The dragon is waking. Soon he will come for his prey,' sobbed the old woman.

Susanowo's eyes met Kunisada's; he saw her terrible distress. Susanowo's heart was hard, but he was moved as never before. He seemed to have no choice; he must save this girl, even if it cost his own life.

A smile lit up the girl's face when he asked to stay the night. During supper Susanowo hardly spoke, but gazed at Kunisada, deep in thought. Before he went to bed, he asked his host to show him round the farm and the food-stores. The old man showed him everything, even his barrels of rice wine. Then the god asked him to summon all his neighbours, with their spades and hammers. Susanowo did not say what he was planning.

Early next morning, as the sun broke through the mist, the peasants formed a dense circle round the house. As Susanowo, calm and confident, appeared on the threshold, they heard a chilling roar, followed by seven more. The hungry monster was on its way!

A shiver ran through the crowd and some ran away, but Susanowo firmly called the braver ones to order. They were to cut down trees to build a barricade, a huge fence with eight openings. The god himself moved the heaviest trunks. Within an hour, the whole valley was fenced off, with only the hatches giving access to the house. Susanowo went to the cellar and fetched eight large barrels. He placed one under each hatch.

The dragon's roars came nearer. Some frightened peasants ran away, dropping their tools. Others spoke their fear: though the fence seemed secure, how long could it withstand the monster? 'What's he going to do now? What's the plan?' they asked. Nobody seemed to know the answer.

Susanowo seemed to have no choice; he must save Kunisada, even if it cost his own life.

THE IMPERIAL SWORD

Suddenly, a head appeared through one of the hatches! It was one of the dragon's. The remaining peasants fled in terror, while Kunisada and her parents took cover in their house. Alone in the courtyard, Susanowo stood sword in hand. Quickly he knocked the tops off the barrels, and the smell of rice wine filled the air.

Susanowo moved back and hid under the farmer's cart. The dragon was suspicious. This new fence troubled it. It beat hard against it with its clawed feet, but could not break it. Then it spat flames to burn it down, but soon stopped. It had smelt the rice wine. Its sixteen nostrils flared at the rich, sweet aroma, and it inhaled deeply. This caused a violent wind in the courtyard, sucking tiles from the roof.

'I'd know that smell anywhere!' growled the first head.

'*Sake*! Rice wine! Yum, yum!' agreed the fifth.

All the dragon's mouths began to water, and it attacked the fence more fiercely than before. But still the fence held firm. What could the dragon do. It could not burn the fence down because the delicious sake would all evaporate.

'I know!' said the third head. 'Let's look through those openings!'

'Go for it!' cried the others, intoxicated by the smell.

But the eighth head, which was wiser than the rest, called them back. 'Suppose it's a trap? One of us should try the hatch first, while the rest stand guard.'

The first head slipped quickly through a hatch, and returned licking its lips. 'It's delicious, the best I've ever drunk.' It took a quick breath and plunged back to the barrel. The

As the first head rose drunkenly, Susanowo was there, sword in hand.

others, maddened by the smell, began to argue among themselves. None wished to wait while the others drank their fill. In the end the temptation was too great, and they all thrust themselves through the hatches at once.

Within minutes, all the barrels were dry. As the first head rose drunkenly, Susanowo was there. He raised his sword and struck off the head with a single blow. The monster started with pain, knocking down part of the fence. Its screams could be heard in the farthest islands of Japan. The seven remaining heads lined up against the young god – but they were too drunk to fight. As one stiffened for the attack, another fell shakily to the ground, causing the first to lose its balance. Susanowo was quick on his feet, and easily sidestepped the dragon's fiery breaths. One by one he chopped the heads off. Kunisada was saved!

As he examined the dragon's huge body, he noticed something stuck in its tail. It was a beautiful sword, left by some unsuccessful hero, perhaps. It turned out to have magic powers, and Susanowo gave it to the emperors of Japan. He and Kunisada were married and had a son, whom they called Okuminushi. The boy grew up to be god of magic and healing. Just like his father, he was a wild and stormy character.

25

YU AND THE WINGED DRAGON

The big golden bear stood on a cliff, shifting from foot to foot as he gazed out over the white-crested waves. His fur was so thick and glossy that you might have taken him for a pampered pet; but a second look would reveal his powerful muscles. He was bigger and stronger by far than an ordinary bear, for he was the great Yu, Emperor of China, in disguise. He had come to this lonely spot to think. His country was being devastated by terrible floods.

What could he do about it? Who can tame the angry waters? He had tried to use magic clay, clay which could expand to thousands of times its size. With this he had built great dams, but always the floods came back. This time, there was far more water than could ever be dammed. All he could think of was to topple the mountains, so that the water would drain off to the sea. For months and months he had been digging a channel, but the task seemed endless, and still the waters came.

The Phoenix and the Dragon

A white dragon and a phoenix were flying across the sky when they found a shining stone. They took it and tried to polish it to make it even more beautiful. After years of patient work, they found they had a delicate, glowing pearl. The fields that were touched by its rays became lush and fertile. The Celestial Empress wanted the pearl for herself, and stole it.

The phoenix and the white dragon searched desperately for it among the stars, and at last they found it in the Empress's palace. There was a terrible argument, during the course of which the pearl fell to Earth. The friends tried to catch it, but failed, and it fell down and landed in China.

In the place where it fell, a beautiful lake formed, which is now called the Western Lake. The phoenix and the dragon flew down and stood guard over it. They can still be seen today; the dragon has turned into a high mountain, and the phoenix into a green hill. Perhaps one day they will awaken.

At last he had given in. Now, as he looked over the waves, he saw something moving in the sky. It was a huge dragon flying his way. It circled around Yu, then gently landed by his side. Yu recognised it and greeted it warmly; it was a water-spirit, which lived in the great storm-clouds. Sometimes these dragons could be bad-tempered, but this one seemed friendly. Quickly he poured out his troubles to the dragon, who offered to help.

'You're very kind, dragon, but how can you help?'

'Like this!' said the dragon, hitting a rock with its tail, which was hard as steel but could twist like a silken cord. The rock broke into hundreds of flying pieces.

Dragon and bear set to work. The dragon broke the biggest rocks, and the bear moved them away. For three years the pair worked on, until just one last rock remained. The dragon split it, and the waters rolled through the channel they had made – uncovering vast acres of flat, fertile soil. Yu thanked his friend the dragon, then chased away the snakes and evil spirits who had lived on the bed of the sea and caused the floods. From now on people could live and work on the new land in safety.

At last the Emperor could take human shape again. He ordered two surveyors to measure the world. One walked north to south, and the other east to west, and they found that it was the same each way – 233,575 steps. (In those days, the world was square.)

His son Qi made friends with two winged dragons, and together they explored countries beyond the skies. There they learned the secrets of science and music, and brought them home to teach their people.

The waters rolled through, uncovering vast acres of flat, fertile soil.

27

GOLDEN DRAGON

Golden Dragon flew towards the Celestial Emperor's palace, where the Emperor's birthday party was taking place. All the Immortals and the dragons were there, singing, dancing, eating – and above all, drinking much too much! Three days and nights later, the party was still going on, but the little dragon was tired of it. He did not enjoy getting drunk, or seeing others do so. So he quietly slipped out, and began to fly back down to Earth.

As he flew over China's great plains, he had a shock. The place was a desert! The crops were shrivelled, the trees were dying, and no people were to be seen. What disaster could have caused such a frightful change in just three days?

Then he heard a little girl crying, far below in a small farmyard. He landed at her side, and gently asked what was the matter.

'We've had no rain for three years – not a single drop!' she wept. Her grandfather had died of exhaustion, trying to dig a well.

At last Golden Dragon understood. A day in heaven was equal to a year on Earth! While the Rain Dragon had been having fun, leaving his work, the poor farmers had seen their crops die. 'I'll see to that!' promised the little dragon. He stamped his foot and took off. On the spot where he had stood a spring of fresh water burst forth.

Golden Dragon returned to the palace as fast as his wings could flap. The dancing was over

28

Masters of Wind and of Clouds came by, and agreed to help. Soon the wind was blowing huge clouds across the sky, while thunder and lightning crackled and flashed. A magnificent storm – but still no rain.

Golden Dragon decided to trick the selfish Rain Dragon. He tiptoed up and bellowed in his ear: 'Get up! The Emperor wants rain – now! Hop to it!' The dragon, half-asleep, rose and tipped over his magic water-jar. The rain cascaded down. China was saved!

But when the Emperor heard about it he was furious. How dare a little dragon give orders in his name! He sentenced Golden Dragon to death.

When the terrible news reached Earth, the people of China were angry. They went into the fields with firecrackers, drums, and big copper gongs. The racket echoed round the Emperor's palace and gave him a headache. Beaten at last, he offered to reduce the sentence. Golden Dragon would be banished to Earth – where he would have to be burnt.

The people looked sad and said they would obey. They built a huge bonfire round Golden Dragon. The Emperor looked out of his window and saw plenty of flames. He watched for a while, and said he was satisfied. But Golden Dragon was really safe – fast asleep on his pile of sticks. The flames the Emperor had seen were only gigantic fireworks which the people had let off, to fool the cruel tyrant and save their little golden friend.

now. He spotted the Rain Dragon stretched out half-drunk on a couch, and roused him to tell him the bad news. The Rain Dragon groaned; then said he couldn't make it rain without the Emperor's orders. Then he rolled over and went back to sleep.

Next, Golden Dragon went to the Emperor's chamber, but the guards barred his way. 'His Celestial Majesty is not to be disturbed!' (He had had too much to drink as well.) Golden Dragon feared he might sleep for days, and all the people on Earth would starve. Then he met the Lord of Thunder and the Lady of Lightning, on their way home.

'Take pity on these poor people!' he said. The couple were sympathetic but could not do much. 'For a good storm, you need wind, and clouds – and rain, of course.' Just then, the

Golden Dragon asked the little girl why she was crying.

The white hare jumped to his feet and bounded forward, then stopped for a moment.

NIE LANG AND THE WHITE HARE

Centuries ago, a terrible drought ravaged the province of Szechuan, in central China. Young Nie Lang was living with his mother in an isolated farmhouse. Every day, he had to cut grass to feed his master Lord Zhou's horses. As the drought got worse, he had to walk further each day to find so much as a blade of grass. It seemed as if the whole country had been baked by the sun. At last, he decided to go where no one ever went, to the summit of Dragon Mountain. But when he got there, he could see that the land on the other side was just as dry as his home. Turning back sadly, he saw a white hare watching him. Nie Lang quietly approached it; it seemed tame and unafraid. But suddenly it jumped to its feet and bounded forward, then stopped for a moment as if inviting Nie Lang to follow.

Nie Lang looked at the hare. It had beautiful fur, and looked healthy and plump. It must be well fed. 'Perhaps it knows a secret place where grass grows,' thought Nie Lang.

The boy followed the hare into a narrow valley. There sat the hare, on a carpet of fresh green grass, by a ruined temple. Nie Lang cut enough to fill his basket. He thanked the hare and set off home.

Next day Nie Lang went back, and to his delight the grass had grown back, as tall as before. And day after day, the mysterious grass was always there to be picked.

Nie Lang began to think. 'Why climb over the mountain every day? I'll uproot the magic grass and plant it in front of my house!' Pulling up the first turf, he found a jar of water. Inside it was a beautiful shining pearl. Nie Lang put it in his pocket and set off home.

That evening he gave the pearl to his mother. Its glow lit up the whole house. For safety they hid it in their biggest rice-jar, which was almost empty. Then they planted the grass in front of the house and, tired out, went to bed.

30

Next morning, Nie Lang looked at the grass. It was going yellow, and he thought that all was lost. But back indoors he saw that the pot was overflowing with rice.

'It's a magic pearl!' he cried in delight. Now they had all the rice they needed; the pearl filled jar after jar. The generous Nie Lang gave some to poor neighbours. When the cruel Lord Zhou heard, he came with his men to find the magic pearl.

Zhou's men turned over the furniture and broke all the crockery in search of the pearl. But Nie Lang had hidden it well. Furious, Zhou ordered his men to kill the boy. Thinking he was lost, Nie Lang swallowed the pearl. The soldiers began to beat him, but ran off when neighbours came running to the rescue.

Nie Lang tossed and turned all night. The pearl seemed to be burning him inside; he had to keep drinking. His mother watched over him anxiously. In the morning, Nie Lang ran to the river and drank and drank. Before his mother's eyes, he seemed to change. Then Zhou and his thugs came and beat the poor peasants, saying they had hidden Nie Lang. Suddenly a huge dragon rose from the river. 'I am Nie Lang!' it roared, beating the river with its tail, to raise a great wave. Zhou and his soldiers were swept away. A terrible storm followed; amid thunder and lightning, Nie Lang ascended into heaven. As he flew out of sight, his mother called him 24 times, and he responded each time with a nod of the head. To this very day, the dragon Nie Lang watches over Szechuan.

The magic pearl made the pot overflow with rice.

31

LAZY DRAGON

Lazy Dragon's job at the Celestial Palace was watching the Empress's stove. All he had to do was keep the fire hot; when it was time to cook a meal he must blow on the coals to revive the flames. Though he was a dragon of little courage, he was proud. He found his work dreary, and beneath his dignity. One night Lazy Dragon fell asleep, and let the fire die down under a roasting sheep. The meat was taken up to the palace almost raw. The Empress, whose stomach was delicate, felt very ill after her dinner. She ran down to the kitchen in a rage and beat Lazy Dragon with a stick. Rubbing dripping on his sore back, he tried to excuse himself:

'This work is too easy for me! I could do great deeds. Give me a more challenging task – something worthy of my talent – and I will serve you well!' The Empress was not convinced by this speech, but she decided to put someone else at the stove and give him a chance. 'Here's a job for you. Go down to Earth and look after the mountains. But take care, people's lives depend on you!'

Lazy Dragon dashed off enthusiastically. But on Earth he found a terrible mess: ravines, rocks and dust. There had been an earthquake; Lazy Dragon had to tidy up all the broken rocks, pushing boulders and carrying stones. After this hard task, he began to miss his old job. 'I'll just have a little rest . . .' he thought – but the Empress woke him smartly: 'Go at once and rebuild Mount Taishan.' He did it with a bad will, moving stones carelessly with his tail. At dusk he went to sleep, leaving his work unfinished.

He did not know what an important place it was. Mount Taishan held up the north-east corner of the sky. But Lazy Dragon, unaware of the danger, slept for days. Sinister crashes came from the mountain, but he snored happily on. The first he knew of the disaster that followed was when he woke up covered in dust.

'I'll just have a little rest . . .'

The mountain he had been rebuilding so badly had fallen down.

Up at the Celestial Palace there was consternation; the sky was rocking under everyone's feet. The Empress had been thrown from her bed by the movement. In her anger she had Lazy Dragon thrown into jail.

When the damage was repaired, she relented and offered him another chance: he was to guard the eastern seas. For a few days, Lazy Dragon took the job seriously: calming the storms and smoothing the waves. But soon he found the work boring. He ordered the fish to build him a magnificent underwater palace. There he flirted with sea-maidens, drank strong liquor and forgot his work.

Terrible storms and floods followed; waves so high that they wet the Empress's feet! She knew what had happened: 'Idiot! Sluggard! You've let the sea take over the sky! Thousands have drowned because of your idleness.' She beat him until the scales fell off his back. But Lazy Dragon was philosophical. Down in the dungeons he slept until his back healed. Then the Empress found him one last job – guarding the clouds, under the eye of the bad-tempered Master of Thunder.

To this day, Lazy Dragon drives the clouds overhead when there is a storm – then sends them away after it has rained. Whenever he falls asleep to dream of his underwater palace, the Master sends a lightning bolt to remind him it's time to think about rain.

Lazy Dragon ordered the fish to build him a magnificent palace.

ANBO AND THE MIRACULOUS SPRINGS

Long ago, on a sandy beach under Cockerel Mountain, lived a peaceful family of fisher-folk. One morning the wife was sitting on a boat and feeding her baby son Jinniu. She was watched by dragons, who lived in a palace at the bottom of the sea, guarded by an army of lobsters and giant crabs.

The haughty dragon-king had just had a baby daughter, a dragon-princess in human shape. He should have been quite satisfied, but he had heard she would be even more beautiful if she were fed on human mother's milk. So the king was watching the shore to find a nurse for her. When he saw the fisher-woman, he rose from the waves like a demon, snatched the baby from her arms and dropped him in the sand. Then he carried the young mother down under the sea.

Jinniu's mother cried for a long time, but at last she agreed to feed the baby princess Anbo. Years passed, and she often thought of her husband and son; but she had grown fond of little Anbo, who was always sweet and smiling. Often she told the little princess stories about her happy life on land.

Anbo grew to be a beautiful young girl. One day she asked her nurse why she had left her home, and was sad to hear how Jinniu had lost his mother for her sake. One day, when everyone else was at a banquet, she slipped away and swam to shore. She was very disappointed. It was hot and dusty, and the people were so poor! It was so unlike the happy place her nurse had told her about.

On the beach she saw a father and son. The young man was bathing his father's back, which was covered with terrible sores. He had a beauty-spot on his right ear, just as her nurse had described Jinniu! Pretending to be a lost

34

traveller, Anbo spoke to them. The old man offered her some fish, then, charmed by her smile, invited her to stay with them and marry his son. Anbo accepted at once; she had loved Jinniu on sight, and saw a way to put right the injustice she had unknowingly done him.

After the wedding the family prospered, for Jinniu, with his wife's advice, somehow managed to make wonderful catches of fish; but the drought continued and his father's sores still did not heal.

On their wedding anniversary, Anbo told her husband the truth about herself. Angrily Jinniu told her how, as well as taking his mother, the king of the dragons had hurt his father. Blindly seeking revenge, Jinniu had destroyed the dragon-king's temple, and the dragon-king had come from the sea to punish him. Jinniu's father had rushed to rescue his son, and the dragon-king had scratched the old man badly, leaving wounds that would not heal. As a further punishment, the dragon-king had stopped all the rain around their home. That was the cause of the terrible drought.

Anbo started to cry. Her husband, blind with anger, sent her away. She returned to the palace broken-hearted. Her absence had barely been noticed, for a year on land is equal to a day in the dragon-world.

While her father was out one day, she stole the magic bottles where the rain was kept. Then she returned to the shore with her nurse, and started a great rainstorm.

Jinniu found his wife and told her he was sorry for what he had done. But then the dragon-king rose from the palace in a surge of huge waves. He grabbed his daughter and stamped his foot; the earth shook and a huge crevasse opened, into which he hurled poor Anbo. Anbo was a prisoner in the ground, and Jinniu could do nothing to save her. She has never been seen since, but since that tragic day, miraculous springs have flowed from Cockerel Mountain, which heal all wounds and cure all illnesses.

Jinniu's mother agreed to feed the baby princess Anbo.

Geshan shot an arrow into the snake's mouth . . .

DRAGON'S DAUGHTER
THE BEAUTEOUS BIRD

Long ago two orphans lived in a little Chinese village. Gelu, the elder, was hard and cruel. He married a wicked woman, who was unkind to his little brother Geshan. One day, the wicked couple sold Geshan for a lot of money to a rich merchant; Geshan grew up to be a strong young man. In time he was to join the army in place of the rich man's son. Geshan who did not know about the plot, was packing his things when an old woman told him the truth. Angered by this injustice, he ran away into the forest.

Nobody dared follow him; the forest was full of strange and frightening creatures. Geshan spent the first night in a tall tree, making a bow and arrows to defend himself and hunt for food. Next morning, he heard a menacing hiss in the bushes. Parting the branches gently, he saw a monstrous snake, about to swallow a beautiful many-coloured bird. The bird trembled all

36

over, but it was unable to fly away, transfixed by the reptile's eye. Its fate seemed certain, until Geshan deliberately broke a branch. Surprised by the noise, the snake turned its head, and the bird was free! It quickly flew on to Geshan's shoulder.

The monster attacked Geshan, who ducked away from its poisoned tongue. He knew that if it caught his eye he would be transfixed like the bird. The bird flew off and perched on a nearby branch, distracting the snake for a second. Geshan took this chance to shoot an arrow into its mouth. He yelled with glee and turned to face the bird. Where the bird had been, there was a beautiful girl. What could she be doing there? She was elegantly dressed and seemed of noble birth. He shyly bowed to her, and was about to go, when she spoke:

'Not so fast! I must thank you!'

'What for? We have never met before.'

'Yes, we have. My name is Pearl, and you have just saved my life.'

'I don't understand. I killed the snake to save a little bird.'

'I was the bird. I took its shape to fly around the forest. When the monster took me by surprise, I could not fly away. Then you came along. How can I ever thank you?'

Geshan blushed with confusion. She was so beautiful! 'I – I'd like to stay with you for a while. But I'm a poor boy, an orphan, with no family,' he mumbled.

'But a very brave one!'

Geshan looked again at the girl. There was something strange about her; she did not seem quite real. What magic had she used to become a bird? He asked who she was. 'That doesn't matter,' she said. 'I'm happy to be by your side.' Glad to have such a lovely travelling companion, Geshan clapped his hands. Then she added: 'My father will be angry if I stay with a strange young man. We must get married at once.'

'But how can we do that here?'

'I'll show you.'

She took his hand and led him to a little

. . . There was a beautiful girl behind him!

temple, deep in the forest. On the stroke of midnight, they were married – with the gods of Earth and Sky as witnesses.

37

DRAGON'S DAUGHTER
A PALACE UNDER THE WAVES

Pearl and Geshan settled down in the temple, without a care in the world. The forest provided all they needed to eat. Geshan had never known such happiness. But he was still curious, and one day asked his wife: 'Who are you, really? And who's your father?'

'I am forbidden to tell you, but soon you will understand,' she replied with a smile. 'Come with me, and don't let go of my hand!' They ran across the huge forest, as if carried by the wind, until at last they reached the wild shores of the great eastern sea. Geshan had never seen the sea before, and he was dazzled by the sight of the rising moon reflected in the black waves.

Pearl knocked quietly on the trunk of an ancient tree, reciting some magic spells. She took her husband's hand again, and changed into a little gold dragon!

'Now I can tell you,' she whispered. 'I am the daughter of the king of the dragons!' Without giving Geshan a moment to think, she pulled him under the water. 'Come on! We're going to his palace!' Geshan was surprised to find that he could swim as easily as walking, and could breathe underwater. They soon arrived at a fabulous palace, with great bronze gates guarded by giant crabs, who let them pass. Inside was a labyrinth of vast rooms, with walls of shining crystal and jade, and crowds of dragons walking around. Some were friendly to Geshan, but others made him wary.

Through the crystal windows, Geshan could see fish swimming past. Pearl had changed back into the shape of a woman. She bowed to her father and explained where she had been. He smiled when she told him of Geshan's bravery, and took it with good humour when he learnt that they had been married – and in a temple too. His son-in-law might not be of noble birth, but he was honest and brave.

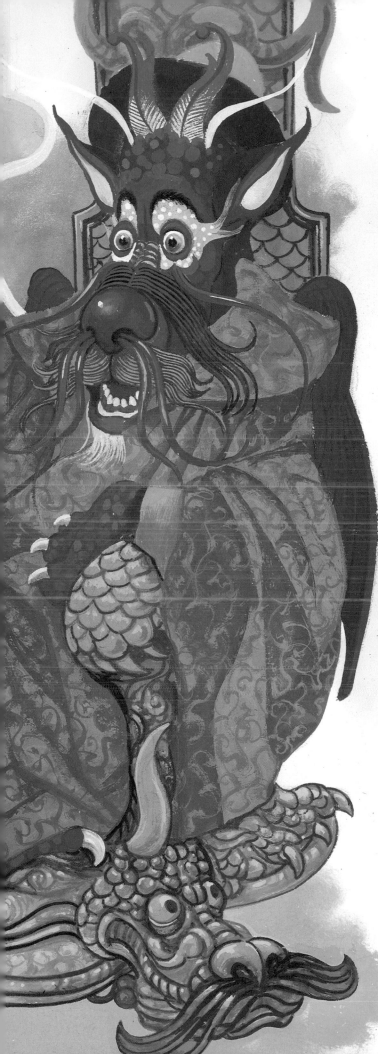

Geshan and his wife stayed a long time at the palace. Geshan could not tell quite how long, because time went more slowly in the dragon world, and under the sea one cannot tell spring from autumn. They had many children and were very happy, but Geshan became homesick. He missed the rhythm of day and night, and longed for news from land. At last the king gave him permission to go home for a short time.

He was shocked to see what had happened while he was away. There had been a long drought. Geshan went straight back to the palace, and begged the king for help. The king was moved, for he knew that the people on land had not always been kind to his son-in-law. Sadly he advised Geshan to take his wife home with him, so long as they visited him often. Before they left, he gave them a beautiful vase that had magic powers.

Geshan and Pearl crossed the desert lands. The ground was cracked and dusty, the trees were dead; they could hardly recognise the place they had left. Starving people begged them for rice, but they had none. That night, they stopped on a high mountain, where they carefully buried the magic vase. Pearl spoke magic words over it.

During the night, they noticed the earth moving where where the vase was buried; a spring was rising. As the days went by, more streams arose from the mountainside, and ran down to all parts of the country. Soon the crops were growing again. Once again the dragons had saved the people of China.

Pearl bowed to her father and explained where she had been.

▷ THE DRAGON'S PEARL ◁

On the banks of a great lake, where no fish swam, lived young Tchang and his mother. They worked a meagre patch of scrubby land which gave them barely enough to eat. One fine day, the young man decided to go and ask the Great God of the West why so much work brought only poverty.

He kissed his mother goodbye, gathered some provisions and set off for the hostile western lands. For 49 days he walked through thick forests. Then, at the end of his strength, he came to a farm, where an old woman lived with her daughter. The daughter was very beautiful, but could not speak. She had been born dumb. The old woman offered him food and a bed for the night; when he told her where he was going, she asked: 'Could you ask the Great God of the West why my daughter can't speak? I cannot go myself, because I am too old.'

Tchang agreed willingly, and walked off for another 49 days through the mountains. When he was almost worn out, he saw a house. An old man who lived there gave him food and a place to sleep. When Tchang told him about his quest, he asked: 'My legs are too weak to carry me there, but could you ask for me why my trees bear no fruit?' Tchang agreed and set off

west. That evening he came to a big, rushing river, with no bridge, ford or stepping-stones. His journey seemed over and all his hard travel wasted.

Then the waters foamed and a dragon appeared. Tchang noticed that his wings were tiny, but in his forehead was a gleaming pearl. The dragon asked why he wanted to cross, and Tchang explained. 'That's a good reason. Get on my back!' said the dragon. 'When you get there, ask the god why I can't fly like other dragons.'

At last Tchang saw the end of his journey; a palace with a thousand rooms high on a mountain. He climbed to the gates and was shown to the Great God's chamber. He was a severe, white-haired old man, in the robes of an emperor. 'Your long and dangerous journey gives you the right to ask three questions, but if you ask more I cannot reply to any of them,' he said.

The dragon carried Tchang over the rapids.

Tchang was disappointed; if he asked the three questions he had promised, he could not ask his own. But he kept his word. Next morning he received his three friends' answers, and set off without his own.

When he reached the river bank, the dragon was waiting impatiently. 'The Great God of the West says that you must do a good deed; then he will give you the power to fly.' The dragon took Tchang over the river, then said without hesitation: 'Since you are so generous and have nothing of value, I'll give you the most precious thing I own; the pearl on my head.' He took off the pearl and gave it to the boy. As Tchang thanked him, he rose up into the air.

When Tchang reached the old man's house, he told him to dig under the lemon-tree. There they found nine golden jars, from which pure water sprang. The trees were suddenly covered with blossom. The old man gave Tchang one of the magic jars. At his next stop, Tchang spoke to the beautiful young girl, and she answered him! Overcome with joy, she kissed the boy, and her mother said: 'Marry my daughter, you will be a fine husband for her!' Tchang stayed with them for nine nights, then took his wife to meet his mother.

The poor old woman had cried so much she had gone blind. He dared not tell her that he had no answer to her question; but then he remembered the pearl. When she touched it, a bright light sprang out of it and hit her eye. She could see again!

The magic pearl also brought fish to the lake, and made the land fertile. Tchang, his mother and his lovely wife lived happily ever after – and each year the generous dragon came to visit them.

THE LORE OF THE DRAGON

It is tempting to link legends about dragons with the dinosaurs, but wrong. The dinosaurs died out millions of years before humans appeared; we know about them today because their fossilised bones have been found and studied by scientists. But, in the Middle Ages and before, people were quite unaware of them. In the places where dinosaur bones are visible above the Earth's surface, people seem to have taken them for the bones of giants (in Europe, they could point to the fact that giants are mentioned in the Bible), not gigantic reptiles. If we want to find an 'origin' for the dragon, we must look for it in the human imagination.

If we look at early pictures of dragons, however, we can see that the idea has been given flesh with an eye to the real world. The long, scaly body of the traditional dragon is obviously based on reptiles, resembling both lizards and snakes. The dragon's head, too, is like a reptile's, a cross between a lizard and a crocodile, perhaps – though it also has something of the wolf, the lion and birds of prey about it. Dragons' feet are often drawn like the claws of birds, while their wings, with the skin stretched out over a fan of delicate bones, must be based on those of bats. Sometimes they have horns – like the Devil, or like snails? The early artists' skill makes this rather mixed-up creature look realistic and utterly terrifying.

Dragons of the Oriental world

One of the earliest pictures of a dragon was found in an ancient Chinese tomb in 1987. Made about 6000 years ago, it is a mosaic of sea-shells set in the ground. The idea of the dragon is thought to have spread to China from the ancient Middle East. The Mesopotamian god Marduk was said to have fought a dragon among the forces of disorder he had to defeat in order to create the world. There is a 2500-year-old picture of his battle in brightly-

A DRAGON IN THE STARS

The constellation of the Dragon can be seen between the Great and Little Bears. One Greek legend said that the hero Herakles slew a dragon which guarded a tree with golden apples. The goddess Hera tuned it into stars. Another story said Hera turned two beautiful nymphs into bears, because her husband Zeus was in love with them. Zeus turned the bears into stars; then he turned himself into a dragon.

A dragon is what you make of him!
Above: This mediaeval statue of a dragon
is in Poitiers, France. Known as
Big-mouth, he is a popular feature of the
cathedral there.

Right: The many-headed Beast of the
Book of Revelation confronts a winged
saint and an angel in a mediaeval
manuscript.

Left: A Japanese view of a sea-dragon,
carrying travellers over the waves. This
dragon has no wings, but strong legs for
swimming.

coloured brick on one of the decorative
gates of the ancient city of Babylon.

European dragons

Ancient Greek myths show dragons as
guardians of treasure (such as the Golden Fleece) or sacred sites. Heroes
often had to defeat a dragon to save
their city. Mediaeval story-tellers took
up this theme in tales of chivalry,
folk-tales and the lives of saints. But the
Greeks are not the only source of
European dragon-tales: the most fearsome dragons of all are found in
Scandinavian mythology. One is the
Midgard serpent, which circled the
Earth, whipping up storms with its tail
and breathing out fire and poison. As a
creature that combined parts of other
animals, the dragon represented chaos,
and the gods who fought it did so to
restore order to the world.

43

Dragons of the Middle Ages

With the rise of Christianity, stories of the old gods became stories of mortal heroes. Siegfried (also known as Sigurd) was the hero of a cycle of stories, which originated in the struggle of the early German kings to fight off invaders. Fafnir, representing the invaders, was a giant who was turned into a dragon to guard his treasure. The list of dragon-slaying heroes is endless, though some, like Beowulf (the Scandinavian hero of one of the earliest English poems), lost the fight. Such tales are set in the wild lands which separated human settlements all over Europe during the Middle Ages.

Devils and disasters

In the Christian era, the dragon became

Above: The Archangel Michael is often shown killing dragons that represent devils, as in this tapestry from the 1300s.

Left: The Venetian artist Jacopo Bellini, who lived in the 1400s, drew these knights of his own time fighting the traditional dragon.

Below: An early photograph of the Tarasque, a huge dragon figure paraded every July in the French town of Tarascon, in memory of a local saint who is said to have killed it.

wholly evil. While the Greeks could imagine a dragon as a wise, earth-dwelling creature, and the Scandinavians could see it as a force of nature, which was dangerous, but could be overcome, for mediaeval Christians it represented the Devil. They linked it with the serpent who tempted Eve and brought sin into the world, and the Great Beast in the Book of Revelation. Dragons appear sometimes carved on the walls of churches and cathedrals.

Dragons were associated with all the great disasters, such as earthquakes and epidemics, that threatened ordinary people. In some places, townspeople held an annual parade with dragon-banners, to

drive out plague, war and famine, those great dragons which ate up men, women and children. Sometimes these parades have survived into our own time.

Worms

The word *dragon* comes from the Greek word *drakon*, which was also used for any snake-like monster, such as a sea-serpent. In mediaeval and renaissance English, it chiefly appears in rather learned books, such as bestiaries (picture-books about animals, both real and mythological), commentaries on the Bible, and saints' lives. The ordinary people preferred to call the beast a worm, and there are many local English legends (such as the story of the Linton Worm, from Yorkshire) in which this word survives. Very often these local dragons live in caves, at the bottom of wells, or in ancient burial mounds, known as 'hills of the dragon'. A hero – perhaps the local squire, or a poor boy in search of his fortune – rides out and defeats the dragon, just like St George.

Saints and kings

St George himself is a rather shadowy figure; indeed he was removed from the Catholic Church's official list of saints by Pope John XXIII during the 1960s. It is not even certain how this Middle Eastern knight came to be patron saint of England.

One church on an island near Venice in Italy displays the supposed bones of a dragon as a holy relic. They were brought there with the body of St Donato, who was said to have killed the dragon by spitting at it.

Lastly, the dragon is a symbol of warlike courage, when, for example, it appears on the flag of Wales. According to legend, King Arthur carried a dragon on his banner; but in fact, the red dragon became the emblem of the Welsh people much later, during the Middle Ages.

Modern fantasy authors have created some fearsome dragons. One of the best is Smaug, in J.R.R. Tolkien's *The Hobbit*.

Another, earlier view of the Beast of Revelation, from the 800s. Here, the artist has given the creature one main head and several smaller ones.

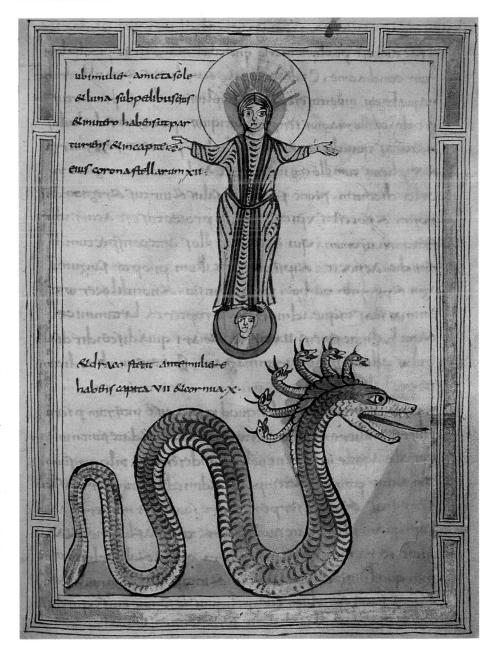

Chinese dragons

The Chinese kept the idea of the dragon as a force of nature, dangerous but not actually evil. In many Chinese stories dragons are the friends of poor peasants. They can be generous, helpful to humans in distress and even just. In Chinese mythology, the tiger, not the dragon, is the most frightening of creatures.

Chinese dragons are nearly always associated with water, and they play their part in the life of farmers. The great rivers, the seas, the storm-clouds and the spring showers are all guarded by dragons. As guardians of water, they usually mean well, but sometimes they are far from perfect, falling asleep, or forgetting to water the crops. If they neglect their duty in this way, the people on Earth are in danger: rivers flood, tidal waves appear at sea, or sparkling springs dry up leaving the people with nothing to drink and the crops to fail.

This richly-painted wooden dragon guards a temple in Burma.

So Chinese dragons can be bringers of wealth or of poverty. Wealth, along with wisdom and secret knowledge, is symbolised by a pearl which each dragon has. Sometimes a human can become temporary owner of the dragon's pearl, which brings untold riches. This is the theme of many Chinese legends.

The sign of the dragon

Dragons take part in Chinese myths about the creation of the world. The tales of the emperor Yu tell how he organised his empire with the aid of a winged dragon. Together they created the first irrigation canals and drainage ditches to bring water to the deserts and control the river's flooding. Many mountains and valleys are named after dragons.

All the emperors of China ruled under the sign of the dragon; their silken robes were embroidered with dragons, and the walls of their palaces were decorated with dragons.

Fireworks

There were dragons in the sky, too. A monster called Kong-Kong made a huge hole in the sky, which was filled up by a great fire-dragon, whose moods governed life on Earth. When he opened his eyes it was day, when he shut them it was night; his breath brought storms and the changing of the seasons. Other dragons chased the sun and moon; if they caught them, they ate them up and there was an eclipse. The Chinese people had a way of dealing with them; they would beat drums and let off fireworks to frighten the dragons, who would let go of their prey, so that the sun or moon shone again.

A SORRY STUDENT

A Chinese fable tells how a foolish man called Zhu Pingman went to a crafty man called Zhi Liyi to learn the secret art of dragon-hunting. He spent three years as an apprentice, and had to pay his master a fortune for the privilege. But he never met a single dragon. The moral is, not to waste time on useless things.

A wooden dragon from Bali, in Indonesia. He was hung above a baby's cradle to protect the baby from evil spirits.

This magnificent dragon is made of ceramic tiles. He has survived wind and weather on a wall in Beijing, China, since the 1400s.

Honouring dragons

Dragons are long-lived; each day for them is equal to a year for humans. But they are not immortal. Some dragons in Eastern mythology marry humans, or have human children, and there are many stories in which a poor peasant meets and falls in love with a dragon's daughter.

Though they appear on Earth, and fly across the sky, most Chinese dragons have their homes under the sea. The four kings of the dragon world each rule one of the four great seas around China.

Chinese people down the centuries have held processions in honour of dragons, and built shrines to them. If it rained, and the procession had to be put off, they would sometimes take the dragon's statue out of its shrine, to punish it for spoiling their day. Today, Chinese communities all over the world celebrate the Chinese New Year with a dragon-procession, in which a group of young men dance in a huge dragon costume.

From China, dragon stories spread to all the countries of the East, and most Asian countries have their own dragons, immortalised in paintings, sculpture and legends.

INDEX